GW00400231

Shh… It Happens

Introduction

Shh…It Happens is here to open up about the things you are too afraid to talk about.

When it comes to sex education, it can seem as though you are left to fend for yourself via self-discovery – often making many mistakes along the way – but it shouldn't have to be like that.

Shh…It Happens is a blog turned book which aims to informally educate people from all walks of life on a variety of topics, from sexual health and sexual concerns to fetishes, and much more. Sex ed doesn't start and stop at condoms, periods, babies, contraceptive pills and vagina and penis diagrams (even though they are a part of it).

The information in this book has been sourced through various second hand research and real life experiences from both myself and contributors to help guide you through the matrix of sexual discovery and sexual pleasure.

Shh…It Happens was created to help destigmatize everyday conversations about sex, genders, and anatomy without judgement; and to talk about the things most sex education books do not.

Breaking down barriers with taboos (pretty much anything sex related) is pivotal to making people feel more comfortable in being open about what is going on downstairs or what they are into in the bedroom.

When you are young, you think you know it all, but as you get older you realise there is still so much more that you do not know about life, and when it comes to sex it can feel difficult to ask for help.

We all deserve to feel comfortable with what we are doing in the bedroom; knowing what we like, and what to do if something goes wrong.

You should not have to learn sex education as you go along; you should be taught it, and know about it - to good knowledge (ideally) - before you even step into that territory.

So I guess this is where Shh…It Happens comes in!

My Story

Like many others, I had to learn the hard way when it came to anything sex ed. My mum left when I was 13 (*quite literally the worst time to leave a young woman*) so when it came to asking the all-important questions regarding periods, sex, and boys, I did not have anyone to help me, except my Dad and my Nan, but asking them anything sex related would have been... awkward to put it simply.

I grew a strong interest in my teenage years about all things sex related because I had a natural intrigue to know more (due to the lack of sex ed in school). I watched porn, I found I didn't particularly enjoy it, and discovered that I was more of an imagination-masturbator. I also hadn't orgasmed from a partner until I was 21, which led me to questioning - why? I soon figured it out. My findings have been empowering for me, so I hope they are for you too.

Throughout adulthood the intrigue continued to grow, and I am still finding out so much about sex that I did not know before. Therefore, hopefully by sharing my knowledge and my findings with you, it will make your venture through life and sex a little bit easier.

As time passes, we are becoming a more open society which is great to see, but we still have a long way to go regarding the progress in sex education. Most people learn sex through watching porn, however, porn has warped people's realities as to what real sex is like, providing unrealistic expectations of what actually happens. You aren't going to orgasm like a pornstar every time you climax, and sometimes you might not orgasm at all – both are completely normal.

Sex ed is so much more than the basics.

Expanding your knowledge on sex education allows you to create more space for a liberal perspective, and helps you to inherit a greater understanding for the meanings behind people's actions, and why they may like or dislike certain things.

The reason Shh...It Happens was created was to educate people about the other areas of sex, to help destigmatize the taboo that surrounds talking about anything sex-related, and to make more people feel open in discussing it - because it is perfectly normal - and after all... it is how you got here, isn't it?

Chapter 1

Condoms and Consent

The most important part of sex is consent. We like to think that sex and consent go hand in hand, but it isn't always like that. There are various reasons why sex may be non-consensual, and in some situations you may have questioned whether or not it was consensual. The absence of a 'no' is not a 'yes'.

In the UK, consented sex is defined in law by Section 74 Sexual Offences Act 2003 as:

"Someone consents to vaginal, anal or oral penetration only if s/he agrees by choice to that penetration, and has the freedom and capacity to make that choice. Consent to sexual activity may be given to one sort of sexual activity but not another, e.g. to vaginal but not anal sex. Or with conditions, such as wearing a condom. Consent can be withdrawn at any time during sexual activity, and each time activity occurs."

To summarise Section 75 Sexual Offences Act 2003 in simpler terms, other times when an individual cannot consent to sex are:

- Evidence that by reason of drink, drugs, sleep, age or physical and/or mental disability, the complainant was unaware of what was occurring and/ or incapable of giving valid consent.
- The complainant was deceived as to the identity of the person with whom s/he had intercourse.
- If there is an assertion of violence, force or threats.
- A child under the age of 16 cannot consent by UK law.
- If the complainant is being unlawfully detained at the time of the act.

This means that even if someone does not explicitly say 'no', if they do not have the freedom or the capacity (they are drunk for example) to make that choice, then it is not consensual.

Another factor to safe consensual sex are condoms. Just like Coronavirus, some of those who have a sexually transmitted virus (i.e. herpes, genital warts/ HPV) can carry it without symptoms, and therefore unknowingly pass it on to somebody else. Condoms do not protect you 100% from sexually transmitted infections (STIs) or pregnancy, but they do decrease your risk by a worthy and sufficient amount.

Chapter 3

Nudes: Nudity Empowers Some and Modesty Empowers Some

As technology and humans have developed we can now take an immaculate renaissance photo of our body, anywhere, at any time, with the click of a button. In recent times the naked body has been sexualised more and more, and coming into the 21st century solidified the evolution of homo sapiens sex drives and sexual exploration all together.

Due to having access to mobile phones with high-quality installed cameras and social media, it now takes less than a minute to take and send a nude. Like anything, when something becomes more accessible – you are more likely to do it. It is quick, it is easy, but that is the problem, sometimes, you can send it to the wrong person.

Are you over 18? Did you know that if you are under the age of 18, and you send sexually explicit images of yourself, you can get charged with distributing photos of child pornography – even though the images are of yourself?

Child Law Advice states: "In the UK the age of consent for sexual intercourse is 16. However, it is an offence to make, distribute, possess or show any indecent images of anyone aged under 18, even if the content was created with the consent of that young person. The law is contained in section 1 Protection of Children Act 1978."

Likewise, the recipient of the image can also get charged for being in possession of child pornography if the person in the images is under the age of 18.

Ultimately most of us do know the dangers of sending nudes online and that is… They can get out. It is a risk in any way you look at it, because everything online is forever – as soon as you post anything – even if you 'delete it', it could be somewhere online, and someone may be able to access it if they really wanted to. Also, with the slip of your thumb you could end up posting it for everyone to see, or sending to the wrong person by accident (I am talking from experience) – there is always a risk involved.

So if you do send your significant other – or anybody else for that matter – explicit content just think about a few things before you do, stay safe, and make sure you trust them. A few things you may want to think about are:

- Do you trust this person?
- Are you sending this nude because you want to?
- Are you being pressured to send a nude?
- Are you sending it with your face in?

To avoid proof of identity when it comes to sending images, be aware if you have any tattoos/ birthmarks/ or any other significant marks on your body that you can be easily identified by. Therefore, if you do happen to send an explicit image, try to avoid including those. Likewise, your face – try and avoid sending images with your face in as it makes it more difficult for people to 100% identify it as you (if an explicit image of you was to be shared). Therefore if your images do get exposed, there is no proof to prove that the content is of you.

People won't always keep private photos to themselves, they may share it with others or publish it on a site – this is called revenge porn. As it goes, we still have a long way to go on thoroughly criminalising revenge porn, both in the UK and globally, but on the 13th April 2015, Section 33 of the Criminal Justice and Courts Act 2015 came into force. This created a new criminal offence of disclosing private sexual photographs and films with intent to cause distress. This is more commonly known as 'revenge porn'.

Crucial to the offence are: (a) the lack of consent of the individual appearing in the photograph and film; and (b) the intent to cause that individual distress. The legislation made sharing of such images or films, a specific offence in its own right and covered all social media platforms and electronic communication. A person who is found guilty of an offence of sharing sexual or private photographs or videos without consent can be sentenced to up to two years in prison, fined, or both.

If you choose to make a video of you having sex with someone and it is to be kept between the two of you – it should be kept between the two of you. Reverting back to consent - if that person consents to the act of being filmed, they are not consenting to it being shared as well. Just because you consent to one thing does not mean you consent to a whole array of other things.

Although there can be things to consider before you send an explicit image – revenge porn is not your fault. Just because you shared a photo or an intimate moment in confidence with someone who you trust, does not mean that you consent to other people being able to see it.

However, you should know that the law states in the UK that it is not revenge porn if the photograph or video is shared for the purposes of journalism. For example, a private photograph of you could be published in a newspaper as part of a news story if the person who shared the photograph reasonably believed it was in the public's interest.

The law also states that it is not an offence for someone to share a photograph or video of you if they believed that it had already been shared or published with your consent and that you had been paid. For example, if there is a photograph of you on a pornographic website, someone might see it and assume you have consented to it being posted and been paid for the photo. They might then share it with someone else. That is not an offence. However if the person who originally posted the image did so without your consent, they may be guilty of an offence.

The bottom line is, it is your body and you choose what you want to do with it, and who you want to see it.

Body positivity and body confidence is not something that should be shunned. Taking nude photos of yourself may increase confidence, and help with self-esteem and self-acceptance. You may not even be taking nudes to send to anybody else, maybe you take them because you want to feel good. Mood is also a dependent factor on whether someone may or may not want to send/receive nudes. We cannot pretend that sending nudes simply is not a thing – because it is – especially in this generation.

If you do not send nude pictures for whatever reason – that is your prerogative and you don't need to explain yourself. Consent is the main thing in any sexual scenario and you have the right to your own privacy. Likewise, for those who want to embrace their nakedness online and in a public fashion you are also well within your rights to do that (as long as you are over the age of 18), just bear in mind the dangers and risks that can surround in doing so.

As the saying goes, 'Nudity empowers some and modesty empowers some.' So whether you choose to send nudes or not – it does not make a difference – we are all human and we all have needs, and should not be judged for that. Just respect other people's decisions and if someone trusts you enough to send you explicit images or record a sex tape with you – don't be a twat and keep it to yourself.

Chapter 4

The Female Orgasm and Squirting: The Truths

One of the most hotly debated arguments when it comes to female sexuality is 'squirting', aka when fluid comes jetting out of a woman's genitals, often with an accompanying orgasm. Not every woman can squirt though, so if you do not think you can, rest assured, there is nothing wrong with you.

It is a no-brainer that the female orgasm is still a mystery to many men. (Should we provide them with daily diagrams of where the clitoris is, perhaps?) But it is not a stretch to say that many women could also use more education when it comes to reaching climax, whether solo or with a partner.

Unlike men, not every woman can cum. Well, not easily anyway. For a woman it is a lot harder. This expectation of women being able to cum and squirt like pushing a button on a machine is absolutely and categorically a myth and only something you will see in porn - there is such a thing called video editing that they like to do (it catches the best bits).

Some women can cum really easily – yes – but most cannot orgasm that easily. According to research, 75% of women cannot cum from penetration alone. Being able to orgasm can depend a lot on foreplay for a woman, and heavily on clitoral stimulation in order to achieve it.

No disrespect to penis-in-vagina intercourse, but penetration is not the easiest route to an orgasm for most women. What move is more likely to lead to an amazing vaginal orgasm? Oral sex - receiving it, that is.

According to a 2017 study from the Journal of Sex and Marital Therapy, nearly 70% of women described receiving oral as 'very pleasurable'. Meanwhile, a third of women said that they need this kind of touching to reach climax.

Right let's try to get the record straight - WTF is squirting? Is it cum? Is it wee? Is it some other liquid your body makes up? Recent research puts the number of women who experience squirting at around 54%. But that same research found that up to 66% of those women experience coital incontinence, or excreting urine at orgasm. And it is hard to tell the difference between ejaculate and urine, says Dr Streicher for Health,

"With female ejaculation, what we are generally talking about is an emission of fluid from the Skene's glands, which are little glands on the side of the urethra," she explains, "Some women do lose urine when they orgasm, but it is very diluted so it doesn't smell like urine. So it's not so obvious what's happening."

Either way, it is just what some bodies do, "One of the questions that comes up all the time with my patients is whether there's a way to make it stop," Dr Streicher continues, "If it's ejaculate, no. If it's urine, there are opportunities to try and decrease or eliminate incontinence. But I get a surprising number of women who tell me they want to ejaculate. How can they make that happen? I have no idea."

So is squirting fact or fiction? Casey Calvert, a porn star, BDSM and fetish expert for GameLink, and a self-professed squirter, thinks squirting is a real phenomenon. She says to Cosmopolitan that if you want to squirt orgasmically, "get very comfortable with your Hitachi vibrator and also get a G-spot toy".

To be clear, a lot of the time when you see squirting in porn – it is pee. Calvert says: "You can't tell (it's pee) unless the girl is really bad at her job and didn't drink enough water and it's really yellow" she continues, "My personal experience is that I can't squirt on command. The porn makers are very practical about it. If you get hired to do a squirting scene, they don't really care what you're doing, if you're actually expressing the gland that creates the real squirt or if you're peeing." So it makes sense that sometimes squirting, like a lot of other things you see in porn – is not real.

Squirting is also a popular fetish, according to Calvert, which is why you see it a lot in porn. It is also possibly what is driving all of the conversations about it. She theorises that it is popular with men because they like to see tangible evidence that a woman is cumming.

Porn likes to create this image that the female orgasm is something you cannot physically miss, with its soul shaking body takeover. This is not true. It is not always that way. On some occasions, some women can't even identify if they have had an orgasm or not, due to other heightened times of peak pleasure during their sexual encounter.

According to ListVerse, research by a neuroscientist shows that many women report having orgasms without any noticeable contractions or violent shaking of the limbs like we would generally expect, and science does not know why.

The high importance that society places on sex, combined with our incomplete knowledge of the orgasm, has led to a number of common misconceptions. However, orgasms are not as simple and as common as many people would suggest. It is estimated that around 10-15% of women have never had an orgasm.

There is also not really a 'right amount of time' for your orgasm to last. In fact, researchers used to think that three to 15 seconds was about the duration of a female orgasm. Then they found evidence that a female climax could go on for 20 seconds to two minutes.

According to NCBI, almost 60% of women ejaculate when they orgasm. However it has been proven that women in same-sex relationships are more likely to orgasm than women who only sleep with men. In a recent study published in Archives of Sexual Behaviour, 95% of heterosexual men reported that they usually or always orgasm during a sexual encounter, while only 65% of heterosexual women said the same thing.

Cosmopolitan states: "Squirting has nothing to do with the intensity of the orgasm. In fact, the women who do it are likely more focused on fulfilling the sexual fantasies of their male sex partners than actually enjoying an orgasm. Many sex therapists actually think that straining to squirt can ultimately damage the pelvic muscles."

And for all those wondering, when the contents of this fluid have been analysed, it is actually – yes – closer to pee than it is to female ejaculate.

Chapter 5

The Morning After Pill

First of all...What is it? Emergency contraception, also known as the 'morning after pill' has long been shrouded in mystery and stigma. The morning after pill is a pill that is taken after unprotected sex (or if the birth control in place has failed) to prevent pregnancy. However this should not be used as a constant alternate method of contraception.

There are two forms of emergency contraception that can be used after unprotected sex to prevent pregnancy. These are: the emergency IUD – also known as the 'emergency coil' and the 'morning after pill'. However, the emergency copper coil, or IUD, has to be implanted by a professional, whereas you can get the morning after pill at your local pharmacy or online.

When it comes to the morning after pill – you have a choice of two different pills – containing either ulipristal acetate (EllaOne) or levonorgestrel.

EllaOne (ulipristal acetate) can be taken within five days (120 hours) of unprotected sex and levonorgestrel containing emergency contraceptive pills can be taken within three days (72 hours) of unprotected sex.

However, even though levonorgestrel containing emergency contraceptives can be taken up to three days after having unprotected sex, they are most effective if taken within 12 hours. The sooner you take it, the better – for both pills. The emergency contraceptive pills work by preventing or delaying ovulation and must therefore be taken as soon as possible, because they are not effective if ovulation has already taken place.

Emergency contraception is an effective option for preventing pregnancy after unprotected sex, but it is not as effective as other methods of contraception and is not recommended for routine use.

You may also want to bear in mind that the morning after pill can fail even with correct use, and it offers no protection against sexually transmitted infections.

If you are sick within two hours of taking Levonelle or three hours of taking EllaOne, you should seek medical attention as you will need to take another dose or have an IUD fitted, due to you potentially throwing up the original dose.

The morning after pill is not appropriate for everyone. You should also check that you are not allergic to any component of the morning after pill, and be wary if you are taking certain medications as that can have the potential to decrease the effectiveness of the morning-after pill.

The Guardian reports that the creator of the Levonelle morning after pill states that it is ineffective in women who weigh over 80kg (12st 7lbs), however the alternate (and more expensive) option, EllaOne doesn't have a 'weight-cap' as such and is effective regardless of BMI or weight.

It is also worth noting that if you are under 25 and live in the UK you can get access to free emergency contraception from your GP and some pharmacies, just call them and ask to find out.

You can also get the morning after pill for free on the NHS at contraception clinics, most sexual health/GUM clinics, most GP surgeries, most NHS walk-in centres and minor injuries units and some hospital A&Es. It is also free if prescribed by your GP or a sexual health/contraception clinic.

Both Levonelle and EllaOne can also be purchased online, however most women don't know this. Research reveals that only 7% of women are aware that it is possible to order the morning after pill online.

Yes, that is correct. You can order the morning after pill safely online. Prices can vary between £15-£35 depending on which one you buy and where you purchase it from.

Chapter 6

Everything Wrong With Porn

Thanks to the internet, accessing pornography is now easier than ever. Long gone are the days of surreptitiously buying X-rated films and top-shelf magazines from 'seedy' sex shops and corner stores.

In 2019 there were over 42 billion visits to Pornhub, which means there was an average of 115 million visits per day. So if you have been indulging in a cheeky bit of pornography, you are certainly not alone.

It is, however, important to recognise that pornography is a form of entertainment - and just like Hollywood movies – the reality of real life is far more different to what happens on screen. There are a lot of things that are 'wrong' with porn, and the reason I say 'wrong' is because of how people are influenced by porn.

Like stated prior, porn is simply a form of entertainment. Here are a few hot takes of what I think is 'wrong' with porn: the lack of foreplay, the pressure on men to last long in bed, the pornstar (fake) orgasm, the 'perfect' body image, the huge lack of condoms, the sexualisation of lesbians, a consistency of non-existent pubic hair, and the sexpectations porn gives the ordinary person.

We have lots of ground to cover but let's start with foreplay. Foreplay in porn often lasts for no time at all, and can even be edited out completely. Female porn stars always seem ready and raring to go from the off, however, for most women, foreplay is the key to good sex.

Frequently in porn films, women seem to orgasm at least once – regardless of foreplay. This can mislead both men and women into thinking that this is the reality, when it is not. Porn is a film, it is directed, it is edited, everything is made to look as good as it possibly can to its target audience – it is not reality.

Secondly, why does nobody wear condoms in porn? Considering porn advocates sex, you would think the people in the industry would use their power to advocate safe and consensual sex; especially considering how many young people watch porn.

Most people begin to watch porn when they start going through puberty, as they then start getting sexually inquisitive.

According to the NHS, the average age for a girl starting puberty is 11 and the average age for a boy is 12. Porn is so easily accessible, and straight off the back, these kids are not even going to know or even think about condom use when it comes to becoming sexually active as they get older – unless they are taught about it. Even then, the way porn normalises unprotected sex is definitely negatively influencing young and naive teens and twenty-somethings all across the world.

Porn can also put pressure on men to last long in bed. The NHS states that a man on average lasts five and a half minutes during a round of intercourse. Some men who watch porn may feel ashamed that they do not last as long as male porn stars, when in reality, male porn stars often use Viagra and other treatments to stay erect for longer, and they often stop and start in between film takes, which would obviously lead to the sex scene being longer than your average.

There is also a huge lack of diversity in mainstream porn regarding: age, hair colour, skin colour, body shapes and sizes. Not to forget the vag-scrimination and how every pornstar has a similarly looking small vagina. Many female porn stars have surgery to give themselves 'designer vaginas' when in reality, vaginas come in all shapes and sizes, and there is no such thing as a 'perfect one' everyone has different preferences and a different version of 'perfect'.

Also, where are the pubes? It seems you only get the bush if you ask for it on porn, otherwise all mainstream videos are traditionally smooth bald patches. Women are not always shaved when it comes to sex, because sometimes sex is random, most women are not having sex to be performing on camera and be watched by millions.

This brings me back to the female orgasm. Porn is an exaggeration, just like how acting is, therefore they enhance their orgasms to make for a better, more enjoyable watch. I hate to break it to you, but it is highly likely that the majority of orgasms you have watched in porn weren't even real. Don't let porn warp your perception of the female orgasm.

If you are sick of mainstream porn, you are in luck because 'feminist porn' is now a thing. Feminist porn hires a plethora of diverse porn stars, so you can enjoy a fumble over more relatable people and sex scenarios. Feminist pornographer Tristan Taormino describes to Cosmopolitan in depth what feminist porn is and how to find it:

"Feminist porn features minorities underrepresented in mainstream porn, so you may see people of different gender identities and expressions, races, body types, or as can stress related to: jobs, money, and other life events. Relationship problems and poor communication with a partner can also cause sexual dysfunction in both men and women.

One of the first steps of treatment is to distinguish whether it is physiological or psychological ED. The causes of ED can vary, and the root cause can be because of psychological, neurological, or lifestyle issues.

Treatment for ED varies from person to person. Some men may find that improving their overall health may be enough to help the ED; other people may require more treatment, such as relationship counselling before they see any improvements. If lifestyle and relationship improvements are not sufficient to improve ED, doctors may recommend medications.

Lloyds Pharmacy's Online Doctor, Dr Gigi Taguri says: "There are four main prescription-only medicines which are used to treat erectile dysfunction in young men: Viagra (sildenafil), Cialis, Levitra and Spedra. You can purchase all of these erectile dysfunction medicines through our discreet online service. They all work in roughly the same way, by opening up the arteries which supply blood to the penis. This allows blood to fill the erectile tissue in the penis, and for an erection to be achieved and maintained."

What men should not do is take an ED drug like Viagra without a prescription, or mix them with other drugs. Just like any drug, Viagra does have its dangers. In an article for Everyday Health, Penny Kaye Jensen, PhD, president of the American Academy of Nurse Practitioners says: "This is a huge problem and not a safe practice" about mixing other drugs with ED drugs. She continues,

"Some young men are mixing ED drugs with mind-altering drugs, such as ecstasy or crystal methamphetamine. This is on the rise and is a potentially deadly combination. There's a reason the ED drugs are intended only for men who clearly need them."

Jensen concludes: "While considered safe, taking these medications in higher than prescribed doses can lead to serious complications."

If you have any causes for concern, contact your GP.

Chapter 8

Living Life with Endometriosis

Having had a few friends ponder the thought as to whether they may be suffering with something called 'endometriosis', it has brought to light the confusion surrounding this condition.

Endometriosis is a condition where tissue similar to the lining of the womb starts to grow in other places, such as the ovaries and fallopian tubes. Endometriosis can affect women of any age and it is a long-term condition that can have a significant impact on your life, but there are treatments that can help.

The symptoms of endometriosis can vary. Some women are badly affected, while others might not have any noticeable symptoms. It can be difficult to diagnose endometriosis because the symptoms can vary considerably, and many other conditions can cause similar symptoms.

With endometriosis being such a common condition yet incredibly taunting and painful at times, I thought it would be better to learn first-hand about it by interviewing those that have been affected. Participant one wants to remain anonymous so we shall call her 'X', and the other participant is called Sarah. If you think you may have endometriosis, then hopefully reading these first-hand experiences will enlighten you more on what it is, what the symptoms are, and how you can go about dealing with it.

How Long Have You Had Endometriosis For?

X: "I have had endo since I was 17, so eight years."

Sarah: "I have had endometriosis symptoms since I was eight years old – which was 21 years ago. I got diagnosed in July 2019. My symptoms eased age 12-18 as I developed anorexia to manage the pain. Upon recovery at 18 the symptoms returned."

I only found out that I had Vaginismus when I tried to have sex for the first time when I was 16. The opportunity arose – parents and younger siblings were away for the weekend, we got down to it, condom on and it wasn't going in…

We tried wiggling around in different positions, nothing was working. Worst of all, it would be extremely painful when we forced it. Then his parents returned earlier than planned, and I found myself running down their incomprehensibly long driveway with the wrong shoes on my feet."

As time went by, she felt nervous when it came around to having to explain her vaginismus to a new partner; one night stands and flings would be even more confused. Making some relationships difficult, well sexual ones anyway…

"There were occasions when I was very grateful that I didn't sleep with someone who I knew I would have regretted. And it was a relief to not worry about pregnancy too much either. I managed this way for nearly nine years after I first tried to have sex."

As for treatments? The contributor recommends that the use of vaginal dilators can help with vaginismus. A vaginal dilator is a plastic shape that should be used one to two times a day to stretch (widen and lengthen) the vagina. They come in a range of sizes, to allow gradual stretching of the vagina.

She also finds that breathing exercises before sex help too, taking slow inhalations to saturate the lungs with oxygen, relaxing the body.

"I am still grateful in a weird way for my vaginismus. In my head, my vagina is this odd prudish lady and she has got way more sense than me! It taught me the value of taking things slowly, it taught me more about my body than I would have known otherwise, and also protected me from some bad hook-ups. So if you are experiencing this, please do not panic and please do not think you are weird. There is a load of more information on it now, and it is much more readily accessible. And at the very least, use it as an excuse to get him to go down on you girl!"

28

Chapter 10

Sexually Transmitted Infections (STIs)

STI is an acronym for Sexually Transmitted Infection. To clear up any confusion, although STIs and STDs (Sexually Transmitted Diseases) are usually used interchangeably, they are not the same. STIs can cause STDs. All STDs are the results of STIs. However, not all STIs turn into STDs. An STI is only considered a disease when it causes symptoms. That's it. That is the one difference. When diagnosed and treated early enough, STIs can go away and never turn into an STD.

When speaking of STIs, Healthline states: "Infections occur when pathogens like viruses, bacteria, or parasites enter your body and start to multiply. How they get into your body depends on the type of pathogen. Some get in through skin-to-skin contact with a person who has an infection, others are transmitted through an exchange of bodily fluids, like semen, vaginal secretions, or blood. Infection progresses to disease when these pathogens cause damage to your cells, and signs and symptoms appear."

STIs tend to be one of the lesser popular conversation starters due to stigmas attached, but discussing sexual health is a must.

The stigma surrounding STIs is still very prevalent in today's society as they can often be seen to be used as the punchline to a cheap joke, or used to insult someone who has multiple partners, but the truth of the matter is – anyone who is sexually active can get an STI. Even if you wear condoms and yes you can probably still get an STI even if you think everyone you have slept with is 'clean'.

STIs are contracted in more ways than you probably realise. Penis-in-vagina and penis-in-anus are not the only way; oral, hands, sex toys, clothes and even dry humping all have the potential to transmit STIs.

The association with not being "clean" and having an STI needs to prevail if we want people to talk about them more openly, and in turn, help to prevent the spread of STIs as a whole.

Condoms and abstinence are essentially the most effective ways to prevent STIs, but being open about your sexual health is also a method of prevention too.

Being open about sexual health can include: being able to talk to your partner(s) about your sexual health status, when you last got checked, and if you have got an STI,

Moving the direction from pleasure to pain... besides pleasure, another function of the vagina is to reproduce, and pushing a baby out of a small hole in your body will indefinitely be painful. So in case you ever wondered - yes, vaginas can tear when giving birth, and it is actually a really common thing, so common that up to nine in every 10 first time mothers who have a vaginal birth will experience some sort of tear, graze or episiotomy (a cut through the area between your vaginal opening and your anus).

Tears can occur inside the vagina, or on parts of the vulva, including the labia. It is, however, slightly less common for mothers who have had a vaginal birth before. These 'injuries' can be minor tears or a longer cut (called an episiotomy) made intentionally by a healthcare provider when, for example, the baby is positioned feet-first or the delivery needs to happen faster. Scary? Yes. Irreparable? Nope! Your vagina is resilient and due to ample blood supply, actually heals quicker than other parts of the body.

Speaking of tearing the vagina, one of the most common sex myths you will hear is about 'popping the cherry', otherwise known as 'losing your virginity' and 'tearing your hymen'. Some women are born without a hymen, but most women are born with a hymen, which is a thin piece of skin that stretches across part of the vaginal opening. Despite what you may have heard, at no point in your life will this piece of skin 'pop'.

Hymens often tear before a person ever has penetrative sex, usually during some unsexy activity like riding a horse, or putting in a tampon. But it is also common for the hymen to tear during sex, in which case a bit of blood is to be expected. Like anything body related, the amount of blood will vary from person to person. However, not having a hymen does not mean you are not a virgin, and that you have had sex before – it is merely a fake construct created by society. You can be a virgin and not have a hymen – for numerous reasons.

Another vagina myth is that your vagina gets 'stretched' or goes bigger after lots of sex. Lots of sex won't stretch it out, the vagina is incredibly elastic, so it always returns to its usual tightness after sex. On the flip-side, nor will it 'shrink' if you go through a 'dry spell' (no sex).

Something that some people may think is a myth but definitely isn't is, 'queefing'. All women have experienced it at one point or another: that embarrassing yet uncontrollable emission of air from the vagina, it sounds like a fart - but it is not. Those little puffs of air that emerge from our lady parts are simply that – trapped air that is being released from the vaginal canal. 'Queefs' can commonly occur during sex if air gets trapped. They are not 'farts' in the traditional sense because they are not waste gases, nor do they emit an unpleasant odour. Queefs really are not a big deal, it happens to all of us at some point in our life.

Now let's talk about discharge. Vaginas are not supposed to smell of strawberries, but they are supposed to have a smell. This should be common knowledge by now, but it is not. The bottom line? The vagina contains a highly specialised cult of bacteria that work 24/7 to keep your vaginal pH healthy, balanced, and at an optimal level to ward off other hostile bacteria. Like other bacteria, these do have a smell. After all, the vagina self-cleanses, so let it do its thing. However, if the odour becomes strong and unpleasant, or is accompanied with an unusual discharge - then it is time to see the doctor.

It is totally normal to see discharge – which may be thin or thick, clear or white-ish – in your underwear at the end of the day (it can vary from person to person). This is the result of your vagina's cleaning efforts. Discharge can also change throughout your menstruation cycle.

Dr Boyle for Cosmopolitan says: "The change in your discharge during ovulation creates a hospitable environment for the sperm to travel up to the egg. If it ever itches, burns, smells foul, or looks like cottage cheese, see your gyno."

The vagina is a truly magical masterpiece, a self-healing queen.

Chapter 13

The World of Genders and Sexualities

The world of genders and sexualities is a glorious yet heavily misunderstood topic. As the world is moving forward in terms of progression with equality in the LGBTQ+ community, it is important that everyone helps to keep that momentum going by educating yourself and others to become more open minded and accepting of what you may not have previously understood.

For those that do not know, LGBTQ+ is an acronym for: lesbian, gay, bisexual, transgender, and queer. People of all sexualities under the LGBTQ+ umbrella may also identify as 'queer', they may use the term 'queer' to reclaim it, as historically many have used the term as a slur. However, unless a person is a member of the LGBTQ+ community, it is generally not a good idea to use this term.

Although it looks like we have come far in terms of the western world, for example gay relationships are now broadcasted on television, as are gay and trans actors. However as of 2023, same-sex marriage is only legal in 34 out of 195 countries worldwide, and it is still illegal to be LGBTQ+ in 64 countries. Therefore, we as humans, still have a long way to go to help get these people in the LGBTQ+ community the respect and rights that they deserve – all over the world.

First of all, the difference between gender and sexuality is gender is what gender you identify as and a person's sexuality, or sexual orientation, determines whom they do, or do not, feel attraction towards (this attraction is typically sexual or romantic).

Sexual attraction typically describes a person's desire to have sex or form a sexual relationship with other people, it also often describes physical attraction, or lack thereof, towards others. Romantic attraction can describe a person's expression of love within a relationship. This relationship does not have to be sexual, and a person does not have to experience both romantic and sexual attraction in order to have a sexuality.

There are a lot of sexual orientations, and people who identify with one or more may find that their sexuality changes over time. This is perfectly normal - a person's orientation can be fluid. They may also sit under an umbrella term but not find a label that accurately describes their experience. Some terms you may have heard more of recently are, pansexual (people who feel attraction toward people of all genders and sexes), bisexual (have an attraction to both men and women), and asexual (lack of sexual attraction to others, or low or absent interest in or desire for sexual activity). For someone who is searching for the perfect word to describe their sexual desires, having a word to call it could take them a step closer to finding sexual liberation.

The misunderstandings revolving around gender identity and sexuality all boils down to education, or lack thereof. People are people. Love is love. As long as the relationship is between two consenting adults, it really is nobody else's business. Discriminating or judging someone over how they choose to look or live their life really says more about you, than it does them. You should be free to live life how you want to, and if you feel as though you aren't the gender you were assigned at birth, you now have the option to change that, and that is amazing.

As a heterosexual cis person you will never thoroughly understand the troubles those in the LGBTQ+ community face because you have never experienced that life. However there are resources out there to help you gage a greater understanding: 'Pose' on BBC iPlayer and 'It's A Sin' on Channel 4 are two really good drama series which educates you on gay relationships, and it takes you back to what being gay or trans in the 80s was like (where it was even more less accepted) and the torment they had to go through just to be able to be themselves.

This follows into why pronouns are important. Gender identity is how a person chooses to identify their gender. In our society the genders that are most recognised are male and female (called the gender binary) and usually it is based on someone's anatomy (the genitals they were born with). This is gender assignment and it is based on an assumption that someone's genitals match their gender. However, gender isn't about someone's anatomy, it is about who they know themselves to be.

There are many different gender identities, (much more than just two) including: male, female, transgender, gender neutral, non-binary, agender, pangender, and all, none or a combination of these.

So why are pronouns important? Even if you do identify with the sex assigned to you at birth, as an ally, it is important to understand the language behind gender-related terms. It is also important to remember that similar to sexuality, gender can be fluid. For this reason, you must keep in mind that someone's gender identity may change over time and that is ok.

Pronouns are important because you are respecting the person you are addressing. By mis-pronouning someone you are disrespecting them, whether you think so or not. By assuming a person's pronouns, you are projecting a message that people must look a certain way to be able to use their pronouns. If you are uncertain - just ask!

We must acknowledge that there are many more genders and sexualities you can explore beyond what is detailed below. So whether you identify with one of these terms or just want to become a better ally, here are 15 terms and definitions essential to creating a more inclusive, understanding and respectful environment for everyone:

Term	Meaning
Agender	A person who identifies as agender might experience an absence of any gender feelings or affiliation. (Remember that 'a' as a prefix means 'absence of something', so agender = absence of gender).
Asexual	An adjective used to describe people who do not experience sexual attraction.
Bisexual	A person who is sexually or romantically attracted to both men and women, or to more than one sex or gender.
Cisgender (Cis)	Often abbreviated to "cis" refers to people whose gender identity matches the sex they were assigned at birth. So if you were born with a penis and you feel and consider yourself to be male, you would be a cisgender male.
Gender	Whilst sex is based on biology, chromosomes, and what doctors assign at birth and write on the birth certificate; gender is a social construct, meaning something that was created by humanity, complete with its own set of 'rules' and expectations. As such, individuals may identify with a different gender than what they were assigned at birth.
Gender Fluid	A person who is gender fluid may always feel like a mix of the two traditional genders, but may feel more

	male some days, and more female on other days.
Genderqueer	A genderqueer person may identify as neither gender, both, or a combination. They do not subscribe to the traditional gender binary.
Heterosexual	A heterosexual is a person who is sexually or romantically attracted exclusively to people of the opposite sex or gender.
Homosexual	Someone who is homosexual is a person who is sexually or romantically attracted exclusively to people of one's own sex or gender.
Non-Binary	Non-binary is an umbrella term for people whose gender is not just male or female. This word may have different meanings to different people. Non-binary is anyone outside of gender, or people who don't fall strictly within the binary at all. Someone can be trans, gender fluid, genderqueer, and non-binary all at the same time.
Pansexual	Commonly shortened to 'pan', a pansexual is a person who is sexually or romantically attracted to people regardless of their sex or gender.
Polyamorous	Describes people who have consensual relationships that involve multiple partners. Polyamorous people talk openly with their partners about having, or having the desire to have sexual and/or emotional relationships with multiple people and often set ground rules for their relationships.
Sex	If we are talking about someone's sex, we are talking about what gender they were assigned at birth, based on external genitalia.

Sexual Orientation	Sexual orientation is completely separate from gender identity. One refers to who you are attracted to (sexual orientation), whilst the other refers to your gender. This is important and often misunderstood. While someone who is non-binary or trans may identify as gay or bisexual, various gender identities can also have a heterosexual sexual orientation.
Transgender	Often abbreviated to 'trans' refers to someone whose gender does not align with the sex they were assigned at birth. For example, a transgender man is someone who was assigned female at birth but is now expressing a male gender identity, and a transgender woman is someone who was assigned male at birth but is now expressing a female gender identity.

Chapter 14

A Guide to Oral Sex

Oral sex... Where shall we begin? Let's start with the basics. Just to clarify, a quick explanation of oral sex is using your mouth and tongue to stimulate your partner's genitals or anus. Like all sex, different people enjoy different things. Phrases such as: 'going down', 'rimming' and 'blow jobs' are some of the many ways of describing oral sex. There are a whole variety of ways to lick, suck and stimulate someone.

A lot of people enjoy oral sex as part of their sex life, but it can be seen as a very personal and intimate action, so it is important to note that not everybody will like it or choose to do it.

You may decide not to have oral sex at all, or you may enjoy experimenting all of the different ways to devour your partner, whatever the decision - it is yours to make.

It is important to establish boundaries and communicate with your partner, so you can understand what you both enjoy, and what you would prefer to avoid. It can take a while to work out what makes someone feel good, the best thing to do is to keep communicating with your partner; ask them to tell you what feels nice and let them know when you are enjoying something.

Some people might not enjoy oral sex because they have concerns about how they 'taste' but do you know whose genital juice tastes like cookies and cream? No one's! We all have our own smell and taste down there, so as long as you are healthy and on top of your hygiene, you should taste and smell just fine. Like anything, if you think you have a problem go and visit your GP.

A 'sex fact' you will have heard at least once in your life is that pineapple can sweeten your juice, but... can it? Though there are no scientific studies that prove this yet, Koushik Shaw, MD of the Austin Urology Institute in Texas, told Health.com that eating foods with higher sugar content, like fruit, could possibly make bodily fluids taste a little sweeter. But that the effects would not be noticeable right away - especially not in men - since prostate fluid in ejaculate can be made weeks or months before it is let out.

However if you have been curious about methods that may perhaps 'sweeten' your taste, Health.com state that eating: pineapple, papaya, nutmeg, cinnamon, or celery can help aid this.

When it comes to safe oral sex, there are a few things you can do as preventative measures: you should avoid oral sex if either of you has sores or cuts around your mouth, genitals or anus, or a bleeding or infection in your throat or mouth (to prevent transmission of potential STIs) and you can also use barrier methods (such as condoms or dental dams).

The best barrier method you can use when giving oral sex to someone with a vagina is a dental dam. This is a thin latex barrier that you place over the vulva. You can order dental dams online or use a condom to create an alternative.

The key to making oral sex safe is to avoid mouth-to-genital contact and the transmission of any bodily fluids. On the other hand, the best barrier method to use when giving oral sex to someone with a penis, are condoms. If you do not like the taste of plain condoms, there are many varieties of different flavoured condoms that you can purchase and use instead. Plus, it might even spice things up a little!

Right, let's get down to the nitty gritty. First of all, when it comes to giving men fellatio (oral sex) if he doesn't finish, do not panic, he most probably still enjoyed it. Men do not need to ejaculate for a blowjob to be enjoyable; most guys don't actually want going down to be the main event either – consider blowjobs as a warm-up.

A man's penis is highly sensitive (similar to the clitoris), so be gentle at first and slowly work up to a faster pace. You can try different tongue, mouth and head movements to see what works best - but never use your teeth.

When you are giving oral sex, you can stop at any time if you feel uncomfortable, and it is up to you to decide if you want to let your partner orgasm in your mouth.

Giving oral sex can be switched up in a lot of ways. Blow jobs can be more than just sucking a penis: spit, use your tongue, lick it, bring the balls in on the fun, and even pop a finger up their bum if they like it (and you are into it too). Get creative.

A top tip is to use your hands as well, this will allow you to control how much of the penis goes into your mouth/throat and gives you more control whilst giving oral sex.

Cara Kovacs, a NYC-based sex coach, suggests stimulating your guy's perineum (located between his anus and balls) by gently massaging him while going down on him, this can be a huge turn on.

However, when it comes to the vagina, oral sex, and giving your partner the 'big-O', stimulating women in multiple areas simultaneously has been known to help them to climax more quickly. So whilst your partner's tongue is at work, have them play with your nipples at the same time.

Nipples can be sensitive at times so when playing with nipples your partner should be gentle at the beginning and then begin test the waters with the intensity and ask your partner if they want you to be more/less intense.

When it comes to giving oral sex to a vagina, pay close attention to the clitoris, but be gentle - there are over 10,000 nerve endings there.

So where is the clitoris and how can you find it? To find the clitoris, gently part the outer lips of the vagina and look for the vaginal opening, the clitoris is the little ball in a hood just above it. By spreading the labia during cunnilingus (oral sex), your partner has the space to approach the clitoris from all angles and sides. In addition to this, Cosmopolitan recommends that you should get your partner familiar with the Kivin Method:

"Instead of having your partner approach your clit in the north end of their oral compass, have them lie perpendicularly, so your clit is now located in the east or west positions. This way, they can lick your clit from the new north to south, aka side-to-side, for what some say is a truly game-changing oral experience."

Another form of oral sex is called 'anilingus' which is otherwise known as 'rimming'. Rimming can be a part of any sexual relationship, whether you are a man, woman, trans, gay, bisexual or hetero - it doesn't matter- one thing we all have is an arsehole.

Top tip: If you are giving cunnilingus do not move from the anus to the vagina as this can transfer bacteria and potentially cause infection.

Communication is key during both relationships and sex, so it is important to always confirm with your sexual partner that both parties are enjoying themselves and to make sure that it is not just a one-sided pleasure party.

When giving oral sex, enjoy it, and show that you are enjoying it. By showing your partner that you are enjoying pleasuring them, they in return, will most likely enjoy it a lot more. Getting vocal in the bedroom about how much you are enjoying yourself will also be a massive turn on for some. Do not be afraid to show or tell your sexual partners just how much you are turned on.

Cosmopolitan has written an article on 35 ways to up your oral sex game (even more). Some of their tips to escalate your oral game are: the use of sex toys during oral play, lube, sucking the clitoris, communicating your needs verbally with your partner, and keeping your undies on during oral and foreplay as it can be incredibly tantalising for both sexes - the ultimate tease.

Additionally, with a little determination and imagination, you can turn pretty much any penetrative sex position into an oral sex position. Just like with intercourse,

Chapter 16

End the Sex Toy Stigma!

Regarding the debate that sex toys have become normalised for women and not men - I must disagree. I think sex toys are still extremely taboo in today's society regardless of the gender they are targeted at, and there still exists a notion of opinions regarding sex toys being 'dirty', 'weird', and 'sexually deviant' when in solo use, or deemed 'unnecessary' when regarding couples sex. This opinion needs to change.

What difference does it make whether you masturbate with your fingers or with a clit vibrator? Likewise for men, why is it 'disgusting', 'desperate' or 'weird' for them to have a fleshlight? In case you don't already know - a fleshlight is basically a fake vagina that you can insert your penis in, to pleasure yourself. If you find yourself wondering 'why do people feel the need to use sex toys?' Well, it is because they feel good!

Obviously, judgement towards the use of sex toys more often than not comes from individuals that do not use sex toys. 'Why should we use them?' some people may ask. My answer is: because they not only help to get you off, and heighten your orgasms, but they also help you to explore your own sensuality too. Using a sex toy is a guaranteed good experience, because you are in 100% control of your own orgasm.

Plus, being single and having a sex toy which can satisfy you beyond human capabilities can decrease the need for seeking sexual pleasure in another person. The stress free way to orgasm... Do it on your own!

Not to backtrack, but I suppose a sex toy can't kiss you and say nice things so it is not a solid replacement for a person – but sex toys are just different; they are a different kind of sexual pleasure all together. After all - they aren't human.

As mentioned earlier, a lot of women rely heavily on clitoral stimulation to in order to climax, so toys can be a great addition to foreplay, and can help you both to reach orgasm (arguably easier).

Granted, the experience of using toys is different for each individual. For example, some women might prefer vibes on their clit, whilst others may prefer to insert a dildo inside of them, or someone agreeing to use a blindfold, but not handcuffs – preferences vary. However with a plethora of options out there, it would be rude to not try before you decide to form a negative opinion.

Some people might not like the idea of sex toys because they may feel insecure at the fact they think their partner wants to incorporate sex toys because they can't pleasure their partner enough, however that is just not the case.

In fact, women feel such a way about their partners knowing about their sex toys, an online survey by a sex toy retailer (TooTimid.com) of over 1,413 women found out that 54% of them hide their sex toys from their partners. Do not let anyone make you feel ashamed for prioritising your sexual pleasure.

This data shows just how prevalent the taboo surrounding the sex toy stigma still is in today's society. If you are embarrassed or ashamed of your partner knowing about your masturbation habits, how is the stigma surrounding sex toys ever going to end? Women, especially, find it a lot harder to cum than men so using a toy can help assist you to climax.

Introducing toys to the bedroom with your partner, doesn't mean your sex is boring and needs 'spicing up' - it can be for many reasons. Being blindfolded can greatly diminish insecurities for some, and a small vibrator may be the thing that helps your partner reach the big 'O'.

Is toxic masculinity the reason men do not want to use sex toys? Is it the lack of sex toys on the market targeted to men? Or are men simply just not interested?

Journalist Zoe Ligon states in an article for Vice, a fair point in terms of sex toy marketing towards men and women: "Women were affirmed by the 'Rabbit' episode in Sex and the City, while men who use sex toys have their entire identity questioned. These days, erotic devices are tastefully marketed to suburban mums on vanilla lifestyle websites."

Even though erotic devices may seem tastefully marketed to suburban mums on vanilla lifestyle websites - they are for everyone. For solo sex, fleshlight's can be incredibly satisfying for men, however, there is often an assumption that follows when a man owns a sex toy for solo masturbation such as a fleshlight.

But why? It is literally the dildo equivalent. If a man buys, or wants a fleshlight, so what? Sex toys are a way of exploring your own sensuality in full control and seeing what gets you off. A fleshlight creates a similar experience to a vagina/anus, but at the same time it is such a different experience because you are in full control of every single sensation on your penis – unlike a vagina which behaves a lot differently.

Using sex toys and the 'real deal' are basically the same concept but two different (yet, similar) experiences – just like using a dildo vs an actual penis. Fleshlight's nowadays have developed and are incredibly innovative, not all look like vagina's –

As fun as threesomes may seem, there is a lot of thinking that needs to go into it. Such as facilitating the correct use of protection when swapping partners, and... just when do they leave?

GQ Magazine states: "Logically, you'll want to have some cool-down and cleaning-off time, maybe offer them a drink, but, are they staying over? If they aren't, and you don't have good public transport links, are you paying for their Uber? If they are, are you making them breakfast? What are you allowed to do with your third while one of you is out of the room?" Just a few things to think about before engaging in your first threesome.

Confession #2 "One of the best sex experiences of my life!"

"It was a Tuesday, and me and my friends ended up going on a spontaneous night out to an Irish bar (with plans to get home at a decent time). It got messy. We then met three guys (all in their thirties) who ended up coming back home with us.

We got back to the flat and drank more for a few hours. Normally I am the first to go to bed so I don't have to be the one to kick anyone out, but because I liked one of the guys, I ended up being the last. Both of my flat mates went to bed and left me in the lounge – alone. One of the guys decided to go home. So it was just me and these two lads.

This is where it got a bit uncomfortable for me, as I wanted to take one of them to my room but the other guy was like 'you go, and I'll stay here and wait'. I thought, 'no way... that's a bit weird?' But then the other guy said 'why don't we both just have sex with you then?' And because I'd never had a threesome before I thought – I am fully up for this – I am going to do it. I think to start with I was quite dominant in who was where, and what I wanted. I never thought in a million years it would ever even happen!

So, the next minute I am giving oral to one of them whilst the other one was having sex with me. Then at one point, I actually was having anal and vaginal sex at the same time – and it was incredible. It went on for ages, all across the living room. I had never been chucked around so much in my life, and the sex was amazing. The two lads didn't want to do anything to each other, so they just took turns with me. I think we continued doing this till about 8am, and then when I woke up the next morning I realised I didn't get either of their numbers and I will probably never see them again. I am gutted, but it is definitely up there as one of the best sex experiences of my life." Anon, 22.

Just like everything in life - with threesomes – there are pros and there are cons. If threesomes are something you would like to try out one day, great - if not – that is cool too.

As far as threesomes go, they are a lot more accessible now, and a lot more common than we think. If they are something you think you would be interested in, do your research, stay safe, set your boundaries and most importantly – have fun!

Chapter 18

Fire and Ice: A Guide to Temperature Play

So, what is 'temperature play'? To put it simply, temperature play is a technique often used (but not exclusively) in BDSM, that uses heat or cold to stimulate the skin and provoke a sensual reaction. Temperature play is often combined with blindfolding and/or bondage to heighten the sensation.

Sex expert Annabelle Knight says to Cosmopolitan: "The main aim of temperature play is to provoke arousal by using the skin's neuroreceptors. Stimulation through heat or cold gives the body a rush of sensations that, during foreplay, is translated into arousal. Temperature play is especially fun for the receiver when hot and cold are combined together in unpredictable patterns."

When talking of temperature play, the first thing that often springs to mind for most people is someone using an ice cube in their mouth to melt on to your warm skin, but as hot (and cool) as that may be, there is a lot more you can do with temperature play.

When it comes to heat, there are a variety of ways to incorporate it into your sex life, but like anything, you need to work your way up to the more intense side of things - and do not just dive straight in at the deep end. A common source of heat used during foreplay is wax, but make sure you use candles designed specifically for sensual play as household candles have varying melting points, meaning that you could get badly burned (and we do not want that).

If you are using a regular candle, and not a massage oil candle, wax play can be dangerous. Be sure to test your boundaries and start slowly. Start with wax that burns at lower temperatures, like soy or paraffin candles, and drop the wax from higher distances (it will cool down as it falls through the air). You can also drop the wax closer to the body, which will make the heat more intense. Some fun, hot and less dangerous methods involve melted chocolate or edible oil which can be heated to your satisfaction and licked off you, making it all that more enjoyable for both parties involved.

If the wax takes your fancy, massage candles are specifically formulated to burn at lower temperatures than regular wax candles, so they will probably be your best bet. However, whilst massage candles are cooler than a candle you would find in a shop, that does not mean they won't be hot – they are just much less likely to burn your skin - so be careful.

Temperature play is a huge spectrum that varies from entry-level kink (experimenting with warm/cold lube) to the extreme, hardcore and very dangerous temperature play (such as cupping or streaking).

Both cupping and streaking are fire-based forms of temperature play and should not be done by anyone other than an expert. Streaking is where fuel is applied directly to the skin, lit on fire, and then extinguished before the skin starts to burn. Fire cupping involves soaking a cotton ball in almost pure alcohol, the cotton is then lit and placed into the cup and quickly removed whilst the cup is placed on the skin. Fire cupping often leaves marks that can remain from a few hours to a few days.

Some other hardcore 'fire fun' consists of: branding, fire flogging, fire fleshing (similar to streaking), and more. However, as previously stated – this should be left entirely for the professionals due to the high risks involved. The people that are at this level have built themselves up to it and most likely have decades of experience under their belt with these practices.

On to the 'cooler' side of things, let's discuss ice. While you can definitely use ice cubes during sex, there are both safe and potentially dangerous ways to do so. Sex educator, Crista Anne states to Elite Daily that before using ice on sensitive areas, you should let it thaw out slightly. She says, "Set it aside in a bowl or cup for five to 10 minutes. While the ice is melting a bit, get things heated up for maximum sensation shift. Beyond safety, this will also allow the ice to slip and slide over skin. Ice sticking to sensitive areas can be damaging and painful."

In general, you should proceed with excessive caution when using ice internally, and it should never be inserted for more than five minutes, according to Crista. However, I would avoid using ice internally.

Instead I would advise a different fun method of experimenting with the cold sensation down there, and that is by chewing a menthol chewing gum and either removing it or keeping it in your mouth during oral sex; it gives your genitals that tingling sensation that you get with ice, but just not as intense – it is a good soft intro into the cooler side of temperature play.

For those who like to use toys in the bedroom, there are a few cool tricks for you too. When using toys that retain the cold such as glass and metal (do not hesitate to take advantage of that) - leave them resting in an ice bucket to change the temperature to either pleasure yourself or have someone else use the toy(s) on you. However, you must always test the temperature on another area of skin (like your inner elbow) before using – this goes for both hot and cold ventures – to make sure it is not too hot or too cold. If you do not have a glass or metal sex toy, fear not – silicone sex toys will work too.

One of the more dangerous things about using ice is frostbite, which can be a real concern when using ice during sex. Some people will find the cold slightly uncomfortable at first, but pain is a sign of trouble when it comes to ice play.

This is why communicating about what you and your partner are both feeling is so important. A 'pins and needles sensation', burning, and stinging are all warning signs of frostbite. Look out for excessive redness or even a bluish tint to the skin, which is rare, but possible. Visual cues mean you should stop immediately and get warm. Keeping a washcloth in a bowl of warm water nearby is a good safety precaution.

Another soft introduction into temperature play is using heated or cooled lube. Lube is a versatile sex accessory, and you can also play with/change the temperature of your lube for heightened orgasms. Holly Richmond, PhD and sex therapist states to Refinery29, "If lube is at body temperature, we're not feeling it. All we're feeling is the penetration or the vibration," Dr Richmond continues, "But if you add that extra layer, that extra element of warmth or cool, that takes things to another sensory level. Stick your lube in the fridge for a few minutes to cool it down, or, get a lube warmer, such as a Touch or a Pulse." Dr Richmond suggests.

With temperature play you must play with caution. Just like cooling and warming up your sex toys, ideally you do not want to get your lube too warm or too cold. Test a few drops on your wrist before using the lube just to check. There are lubes for just about everything - and that includes temperature play. Have fun, but stay safe, communicate and know your limits.

Chapter 19

Explained: The Spit Fetish

After sifting through various articles about men with a saliva fetish asking women on the street to spit in jars, filming it, and later swallowing it, and then (sometimes) getting arrested – I came to the realisation that the spit fetish and saliva fetish are two very different, separate kinks/fetishes.

The spit fetish is usually based on the foundations of the dominant and submissive role partaken in BDSM; whereas the saliva fetish is more about the messy and wet side of things.

BDSM has many umbrella categories and spit is one of them. However BDSM and spit fetishes are not mutually exclusive - you can have one without the other.

In short, a spit fetish is when a person gets aroused by being spit on, or spitting on someone else. The person doing the spitting is usually the dominant, and the person being spat on is usually the submissive.

Is a spit fetish the same as a saliva fetish? No. Although both are based on the same subject, a saliva fetishist gets off on the feel, look and sensation of the saliva on their skin. Someone with a spit fetish likes the humiliation aspect of being spit on, or being the dominant person doing the spitting.

So why do people like this? The act of someone spitting in your mouth, or spitting on your face/ body/ private parts can feel similar to the consistency of cum, which could be one reason why someone may desire to be spat on in the bedroom.

Many of the information online about spitting fetishes see parallels between the act of spitting and the act of ejaculation – particularly in relation to 'facials' (i.e. the act of ejaculating onto someone's face) and the act of bukkake (i.e. the act of several/many men simultaneously ejaculating onto someone's face and/or body).

As for the person doing the spitting, it is usually a dominant action – the 'you're below me' attitude that is associated with spitting – linking it to be a degradation and humiliation kink. For the dominant, the appearance of the spit combined with messed up make-up can be a turn on (making someone look like a hot mess) but obviously it is not for everyone.

If you would like to try it out make sure you do not get spit in your partner's eye as it will most likely sting, go bloodshot, and could create room for infection. (I am speaking from experience here). So... avoid the eyes!

If you have desire to be spat on, this is usually associated with you seeking domination from the spitter/ having the need to be sexually humiliated. If your kink involves aspects of humiliation and degradation, spitting can be the perfect addition to that kind of dynamic.

On the other hand, those with a saliva fetish are usually turned on by qualities in the spit - its lubricating silkiness, its wetness, its scent, or even whose mouth it comes from. Saliva fetishists may like to rub their hands, face, mouth, and genitals in the substance for the tactile sensations and the essence of the saliva donor.

Many different bodily substances have formed the basis of paraphilic and/or fetishist behaviour over time including urine (urophilia), faeces (coprophilia), blood (menophilia and clinical vampirism), and breast milk (lactophilia).

However, one bodily fluid that has not really been the subject of scientific research is saliva (in relation to saliva and spit fetishes).

Compared to all other paraphilic and fetishist behaviours concerning sexual arousal to human bodily fluids, there is significantly less written about saliva and spitting fetishes. Whether academic and/or clinical research is needed is – at present – debatable.

If this is something you would like to try out, it is extremely important to negotiate this with a partner before you begin (like anything new you want to try) as some people might not enjoy this kind of play. However, more people than you might think may have had fantasies about this kind of play. According to research from Justin Lehmiller's book, 'Tell Me What You Want', roughly 43% of men and 35% of women have fantasised about spit during sex.

Get wet!

Chapter 20

The Foot Fetish

Now for some reason, a sense of dread goes through some people when they hear the words 'foot fetish' and for others, well... They get excited. I think the sense of dread comes from the fear of the unknown most times, you do not know what to expect, you do not know if you will like it, and you do not know what others – or your partner – may think.

Most of the time, the sense of disgust or dread is just from pure ignorance. You are uneducated on the topic, but that is ok. Like any fetish, this is not going to be for everyone. You might not be a fan, and have no room for changing your perspective, and that is fine. However, if you can understand it a bit more, perhaps your judgement of disgust when you next come across someone with a foot fetish – will be no longer.

Heathline.com explains that: "A foot fetish is a sexual interest in feet. In other words, feet, toes, and ankles turn you on. This particular preference for feet can vary from person to person. Some people are turned on just by looking at feet. Others may find painted nails, jewellery, or other adornments appealing. Still, others get sexual satisfaction in foot treatments, such as massaging or worshipping feet."

So why are people attracted to feet? People usually associate those who are into feet with men who like to be dominated, but that is not always the case. Your partner, or even yourself having a foot fetish does not mean they/you want to submit to a findom and pay them loads of money to worship their feet. I mean it might do - but not everyone's fantasies are that extreme.

Some people who are into feet just want to caress your feet along with the rest of your body, so they are touching every part of you, making the contact (and whole experience) more sensual and intimate.

Your feet are covered with nerve endings, and nerve endings equal greater, often more intense, sensations making them rather sensitive. Tickling, rubbing, and massaging may all feel immensely better on feet.

New York-based psychotherapist Dulcinea Pitagora a.k.a 'The Kink Doctor' explains to Vice how foot fetishes could possibly result from cross-wiring in the brain between feet and the genital parts:

Top tip: Always choke squeezing the sides of the throat NEVER from applying pressure downwards to your partner's windpipe.

Why do people like it then? As well as the psychological effects of being choked such as submission and power play, there is actually a science behind it. There are physiological reasons why someone may enjoy being choked: when you are being choked you are restricting the oxygen to your brain, which will make you feel lightheaded, but once that pressure is released and oxygen and blood begin to flow again you will feel a different kind of rush, this is one caused by a release of dopamine and serotonin (the feel good hormones).

Another kink that is often associated with BDSM is spanking. Spanking can be pleasurable for many reasons: control, powerplay, roleplay, or the pleasure derived from a touch of pain. Spanking can be cheeky and playful or it can be used as a punishment in roleplay, but either way (if you are into it) it is fun – however it is done.

If you are planning on incorporating some spank-play into your sex life, discover your limits and find your feet before you dive into the deep end. Start off with a hand doing the spanking (to see if you like it), then maybe move forwards to a toy like a crop, and experiment from there onwards onto: paddles, floggers, whips etc…

The pain/pleasure dynamic can often be quite overwhelming due to how highly stimulating it is, which means that aftercare is imperative. It is vital that after a BDSM scene you talk about what happened and that you were ok with what went on, and that emotionally you are comforted.

Aftercare is not just emotional support, but physical too. Tend to your partner's bruises, rub some cream on them, give them a massage, go get them a drink, have a cuddle etc…The more intense the play, the more important safe practice and aftercare is. This should be standard in every sexual practice but especially one involving powerplay and/or degradation.

A certified sex coach and sexologist Gigi Engle says in an article for Men's Health that: "Aftercare is great in all sexual experiences because it takes a person's emotional well-being into consideration."

Tie me up Daddy!

Chapter 22

Water Sports: Everything You Need to Know

'Water sports' or scientifically known as 'urolagnia' is an extremely common kink, and is not what it first appears... Aren't water sports games that you play in a pool? A pool of someone's pee – yes.

Water sports is the sexual engagement with urine, be that with your own or a partner's. A YouGov survey of 2,073 UK adults revealed the top 10 fetishes in the UK, and urolagnia was voted as Britain's 9th biggest sexual fetish.

Like most kinks, there are far more people who are interested in this sort of play than are willing to disclose it. Urolagnia still remains an extremely taboo kink in today's society, but the forbidden aspect of this fetish can sometimes increase the excitement for participants.

Water sports go way beyond a golden shower. Water sports can mean: peeing on your partner, in front of your partner, near your partner, in your partner, or having your partner pee on/near/in front of/ inside of you. No hard and fast rules here except that it definitely involves pee.

Speaking to Cosmopolitan, Samantha Manewitz, a sex therapist who specialises in working with alt-sex and kink communities, said: "There's often a component of dominance and submission in the act of peeing on a partner, or having a partner pee on you. But for others, golden showers are just a fetish that gets them aroused and they don't have any interest in the power exchange aspect of urinating in front of a partner."

She goes on to further state other wants and desires for the need of urine in sex play and in her practice, she found that people are into water sports for a variety of reasons: "Water sports can foster trust and intimacy; there is vulnerability both in having a partner pee in your presence and allowing yourself to be peed on," she continues, "There is also something about exchanging bodily fluids in general that can be hot for some. The fact that it is 'wrong' and 'dirty' can be a turn on in, and of itself."

Havelock Ellis was an English doctor who studied human sexuality in the early 20th century. He was one of the first to talk about this fetish and also to admit that he had this fetish. He thought the fetish had emerged from various incidents in his childhood and adolescence where he witnessed his mother urinating. Lots of people with

In most instances my advice is to just carry on as normal, as long as nobody is in pain. A little bit of blood shouldn't stop you from receiving and enjoying pleasure (unless someone has an innate fear of blood of course).

Period or no period shouldn't determine sex or no sex. Go for it!

Chapter 24

Anal Sex: Shit... Happens

Here you have it. The inspiration behind the name of Shh...It Happens shall be revealed. The name comes not only from shit happening in life, but from actual shit happening during sex. Shit...Happens! And if you want to engage in anal sex, then you best get used to that thought.

The main struggle I have faced is the lack of consideration from my partner when it comes to anal sex, which has since put me off engaging in it again. I presume most women have experienced this? Tried it once, and thought nope - never again. You might also not have even been able to get to the stage of actually trying it, because just the tip going in hurt too much.

Expectations Vs Reality: Despite what you may have seen in porn or heard from your friends, anal sex isn't something that can be done without lots of lube, lots of foreplay and a hefty amount of communication. Please do not force entry into the back passage, this not only causes a sharp stinging pain that then proceeds to hurt for ten minutes, but it can also cause tears.

So for your own safety, and your partners, wear a condom, make sure they are lubed up and make sure they are ready for you. Communication is key. 'Does that hurt?'/ 'Does that feel good?'/ 'How is it?'/ 'Are you comfortable?'/ 'Can I go faster?' /'Do you want me to go slower?' etc...

Treat people how you want to be treated. If you were to be penetrated in your tiny sphincter would you want someone just going straight in? Dry? No. You most definitely would not. Treat your partner's holes how you would want yours treated. Plenty of lube, foreplay, and communication is the key to fun anal sex.

While yes, the ol' 'sorry I slipped and almost went into the wrong hole' happens sometimes, it is unlikely that without a load of lube, your partner won't be able to actually penetrate you (comfortably) all the way in.

The rumours are true: Anal does have the possibility of getting messy. Like anything sex related, when you are swapping bodily fluids, unwrapping condoms, using lube, there is the potential to stain or make a mess. If you want extra peace of mind, make sure the surface you and your partner engage on is comfortable and washable.

You can make anal sex easier for yourself by anal training or gradually introducing larger and larger toys into your anus to train your muscles to get used to the feeling of something going up there. But be careful because unlike the vagina, what goes up the bum might not come out.

But like any other sex act, if things start to hurt in a way that is no longer fun, you should stop. Pain most commonly comes from anal fissures, or little tears in the tissue around the anus, which is very thin and delicate. A good way to remedy that is using lots of lube and starting with smaller objects, rather than big ones. Anal tears should heal within a few days but may cause a bit of mild discomfort when you are going to the toilet.

Unlike the vagina, the anus lacks lubrication. When a woman is aroused, the vagina provides its own lubricant for sex; the anus however, does not. That means you have to provide it. Penetration without lubrication can tear the delicate tissue inside the anus, which can lead to pain and bleeding. No 'Oops! It slipped!' excuses here - as that would be a major violation of trust and consent.

When it comes to anal and lube, there are plenty of options. The best lubes for anal sex are the thicker lubricants as they don't dry out as quickly.

PSA: DO NOT USE NUMBING CREAMS!

Sex Educator Wendasha Jenkins Hall said to Cosmopolitan that you should, "Avoid numbing creams. I know they are tempting, but pain is your body's way of letting you know something is wrong. If your anus is numb, you can't tell if any of your activities are causing damage. You can't feel if you need more lube or if your body is tightening up to the penetration or impact."

Shit happens... just make sure you clean it up. Medical Director Lauren Streitcher said to Women's Health: "Anal sex can be pleasurable as it gets your pelvic floor stimulated and contracting – which in turn will get you to poop." If there's poop there, there's a chance it will make its way out.

How do you prevent any dark messes, you may wonder? If you have one anal sex mantra, let it be, "make sure you're not due to poo". Sexologist Juliet Allen states ro Women's Health, that to prevent any poop disasters, you should avoid eating fatty and spicy foods. If it does happen, your partner must appreciate it is a possible consequence of the act, and therefore, not make you feel embarrassed. Just clean yourselves up!

Anal douching isn't just for the gays! Anybody who wants to engage in anal play, and is worried about faeces, douching will give you a bit of reassurance to say the least.

Douching is basically the act of flushing your rectum out with water. You can use several objects to achieve this or just rinse it with a shower head.

Whether giving or receiving, male or female, precautions still need to be taken. You are at risk of STI's anytime you engage in skin on skin contact, so to help prevent the transmission – use condoms. Even if a woman is pegging a man - STIs can be carried on sex toys too.

Also, if you are monogamous, STIs aside, using a condom prevents bacteria from the bowels spreading anywhere else, so yeah – just use a condom. You should never use the same condom from anal to vaginal penetration for obvious reasons. No one wants poop in their vagina.

'Pegging' is a fetish that has come more to the foreground in recent years. Pegging is where a woman penetrates a man up his anus with a strap-on penis. If you are interested in this, you should always engage in anal foreplay before you go in. Try having your partner rim you, and use a finger or two before using plenty of lube on both you, and on the toy to assure the lubrication is there to insert the dildo – just as you would when preparing a woman for anal sex.

The thing with anal sex is people (mainly heterosexual men) think they can just go straight in. Urm, no? Just like pegging, the anus needs to be prepared. Just because it is a woman's anus does not mean that it is any different to a mans in the way it functions. For pleasurable anal sex, a lot of lube and a lot of foreplay and patience is needed. If you don't want to do any of that, then you're not going to end up having anal sex.

Be patient, be kind, respect one another's boundaries and – mess aside – have fun!

And remember, Shit Happens.

Acknowledgments

After what has felt like an eternity, we are finally finished. Writing a book was not as simple as I initially assumed, but it has definitely been worth it, and even if this book helps just one person, then it has done its job. However, there are a few people who have helped me to create this book and they deserve a huge thank you.

Firstly, I would like to thank every single person who has ever read a shit happens blog post, because without any blog readers I am pretty sure this book would have never have even been written. The readers gave me the motivation and encouragement to go one step further than the blog, and start writing what would later become my first book. Without you, this would not have been possible.

Secondly I would like to thank Jess Ly for her designing the book's front cover. Jess is a good friend of mine that I have known for around five years. She is a sensational artist and tattooist so I collaborated with her on designing my first book cover. We decided to design the lips and finger on the front cover based on me, so Jess took a photo and after a few redrafts, the cover was finished. The book cover turned out greater than I could have ever imagined, or ever done myself. Jess, you are amazing.

I would also like to thank my Nan and Dad for always supporting me on my creative endeavours, and although you couldn't help me much back in the day (regarding sex ed) - look at me now! Also, I am sorry my first book has to be about sex but we all know I am not the type to sit and write about paint drying. Your endless love and support for me and my career doesn't get overlooked, trust me.

Sena Tokel, housemate, best friend, lawyer, ear, proof-reader and my personal cheerleader, thank you for always rooting for me, listening to me read out my writings out loud over and over again, making sure I am not publishing anything illegally, keeping me sane (and insane), and for your open-mindedness attitude towards life and everything that I do; constantly making me strive to be the best I can be. You more than anyone know how much time and effort has gone into writing this book and putting it all together.

Lastly I would like to thank anyone who has contributed to my writing by letting me interview them, and allowing me to ask them some very personal questions. This aspect really adds to the book, and the message I was trying to spread; whatever you are going through, you most probably are not alone. To have the courage to come forward and trust me with information that most people would probably take to the grave with them, for the sake of sharing their own experiences for the greater good, is honestly admirable and I have an abundance of gratitude for everyone who contributed their experiences in both the blog, and in the book.

References

Chapter 1: Condoms and Consent

1. CPS. 2021. Rape and Sexual Offences - Chapter 6: Consent. CPS.gov. https://www.cps.gov.uk/legal-guidance/rape-and-sexual-offences-chapter-6-consent
2. LawTeacher. N.d. Sexual Offenses Lecture. LawTeacher. https://www.lawteacher.net/lectures/criminal-law/sexual-offences/
3. NHS. N.d. What is Consent?. NHS. https://www.nhs.uk/about-the-nhs-website/professionals/healthandcareprofessionals/child-sexual-exploitation/documents/consent-information-leaflet.pdf
4. Rape Crisis. N.d. What is sexual consent? RapeCrisis.Org. https://rapecrisis.org.uk/get-informed/about-sexual-violence/sexual-consent/
5. Stonehouse, Rachel. 2021. Stealthing: 'I didn't realise it's rape until it happened to me'. BBC. https://www.bbc.co.uk/news/newsbeat-57618003

Chapter 2: Pubic Hair - Yes or No?

1. Austin, Emma. 2019. Not Every Woman Can Grow a Full Bush. Believe me, I've Tried. Medium.com. https://medium.com/love-emma/not-every-woman-can-grow-a-full-bush-9dae9f167b75
2. Chesak, Jennifer. 2019. The Carpet Doesn't Always Match the Drapes — and 19 Other Pubic Hair Truths. Healthline.com. https://www.healthline.com/health/healthy-sex/pubic-hair#12
3. Harvey, Olivia. 2019. How much hair is normal down there? We asked doctors about this and other pube-related questions. HelloGiggles. https://hellogiggles.com/lifestyle/how-much-hair-is-normal-down-there-things-you-should-know-about-pubic-hair/
4. Pai, Deanna. 2018. 10 Celebrities Who Are All About Their Bush: Let it grow! Glamour Magazine. https://www.glamour.com/gallery/celebrities-with-pubic-hair
5. Valenti, Lauren. 2021. Why Go Back to Waxing? How to Embrace the Full Bush. Vogue. https://www.vogue.com/article/how-to-grow-out-and-take-care-of-pubic-hair-au-naturale-trimming-ingrown-hairs-exfoliating-cleansing

Chapter 3: NUDES: Nudity Empowers Some and Modesty Empowers Some

1. Agate, Jennifer and Ledward, Jocelyn. 2017. "Revenge Porn" and Section 33: The Story so Far. Footanstey. https://www.footanstey.com/article/revenge-porn-and-section-33-the-story-so-far/
2. Rawson, Colin. 2021. What Is the Law on Revenge Porn? Stephensons.co.uk. https://www.stephensons.co.uk/site/blog/criminal-justice-blog/what-is-the-law-on-revenge-porn
3. Rights of Women. 2016. Revenge porn, online abuse and the law. Rightofwomen.org. https://rightsofwomen.org.uk/get-information/violence-against-women-and-international-law/revenge-porn-online-abuse-and-the-law/

Chapter 4: The Female Orgasm and Squirting: The Truths

1. Arter, Jennifer. Dodge, Brian. Fu,Tsung-Chieh. Herbenick, Debby. Sanders, Stephanie. 2017. Women's Experiences With Genital Touching, Sexual Pleasure, and Orgasm: Results From a U.S. Probability Sample of Women Ages 18 to 94. TandFOnline. https://www.tandfonline.com/doi/abs/10.1080/0092623X.2017.1346530
2. Breslaw, Anna. 2017. Sex Talk Realness: Is Squirting Fake?. Cosmopolitan. https://www.cosmopolitan.com/sex-love/advice/a5085/squirting-sex-realness/
3. Castleman, Michael. 2009. The Most Important Sexual Statistic: Intercourse is not the key to most women's sexual satisfaction. Psychology Today. https://www.psychologytoday.com/us/blog/all-about-sex/200903/the-most-important-sexual-statistic
4. Frederick, David. Garcia, Justin. Lloyd, Elisabeth. St. John, Kate. 2017. Differences in Orgasm Frequency Among Gay, Lesbian, Bisexual, and Heterosexual Men and Women in a U.S. National Sample. SpringerLink. https://link.springer.com/article/10.1007/s10508-017-0939-z
5. Kratochvi, S. 2013. The Duration of Female Orgasm. PubMed. https://pubmed.ncbi.nlm.nih.gov/8269524/
6. Mateo, Ashley. 2017. 10 Mind-Blowing Facts About the Female Orgasm. Health.com. https://www.health.com/condition/sexual-health/female-orgasm-facts
7. McIntosh, James. 2018. Everything you need to know about orgasms. Medical News Today. https://www.medicalnewstoday.com/articles/232318
8. Pastor, Zlatko. 2013. Female ejaculation orgasm vs. coital incontinence: a systematic review.PubMed. https://pubmed.ncbi.nlm.nih.gov/23634659/

9. Sharma, Himanshu. 2019. 10 Fascinating Facts About The Female Orgasm. Listverse. https://listverse.com/2019/06/25/10-fascinating-facts-about-the-female-orgasm/

Chapter 5: The Morning After Pill

1. Harvey-Jenner, Catriona. 2017. The one important thing you didn't know about the morning after pill: Your weight could affect its effectiveness after all. Cosmopolitan. https://www.cosmopolitan.com/uk/body/health/a9206892/big-catch-morning-after-pill-weight-effectiveness/
2. NHS. 2020. Where Can I Get Emergency Contraception?. NHS. https://www.nhs.uk/conditions/contraception/where-can-i-get-emergency-contraception/
3. Planned Parenthood. N.d. Which kind of emergency contraception should I use?. PlannedParenthood. https://www.plannedparenthood.org/learn/morning-after-pill-emergency-contraception/which-kind-emergency-contraception-should-i-use
4. Sharkey, Lauren. 2020. Yes, Plan B Has a Weight Limit — Here's What It Means for You. Healthline.com. https://www.healthline.com/health/healthy-sex/plan-b-weight-limit#short-answer

Chapter 6: Everything Wrong with Porn

1. Breslaw, Anna. 2013. So, What Is Feminist Porn? Find Out From a Woman Who Makes It. Cosmopolitan. https://www.cosmopolitan.com/sex-love/news/a16343/tristan-taormino-feminist-porn-interview/
2. Felix, Dr.. N.d. Porn vs. Reality. Dr. Felix.https://www.drfelix.co.uk/porn-reality/
3. Frederick, David. Garcia, Justin. Lloyd, Elisabeth. St. John, Kate. 2017. Differences in Orgasm Frequency Among Gay, Lesbian, Bisexual, and Heterosexual Men and Women in a U.S. National Sample. SpringerLink. https://link.springer.com/article/10.1007/s10508-017-0939-z
4. NHS. 2018. Stages of puberty: what happens to boys and girls. NHS. https://www.nhs.uk/live-well/sexual-health/stages-of-puberty-what-happens-to-boys-and-girls/
5. PornHub Insights. 2019. The 2019 Year in Review. Pornhub. https://www.pornhub.com/insights/2019-year-in-review

Chapter 7: Erectile Dysfunction

1. Duncan, Conrad. 2019. Up to half of men under 50 suffer from erectile dysfunction, research claims. The Independent. https://www.independent.co.uk/news/health/erectile-dysfunction-impotence-rates-viagra-causes-heart-disease-research-a8985216.html
2. Espinosa, Dr. Geo. N.d. The Dangers of Taking Viagra When You Don't Need It. Easy Health Options. https://easyhealthoptions.com/the-dangers-of-taking-viagra-when-you-dont-need-it/
3. Fletcher, Jenna. 2020. How does age affect erectile dysfunction? Medical News Today. https://www.medicalnewstoday.com/articles/316215
4. Godman, Heidi. 2019. Erectile Dysfunction (ED) in Young Men: Causes and Treatments. Healthline https://www.healthline.com/health/erectile-dysfunction/young-men#physical-causes
5. Medzino. 2019. Erectile dysfunction in your 20s. Medzino. https://www.medzino.com/us/health-center/erectile-dysfunction-in-your-20s/
6. Myers, Wyatt. 2011. Young Men Get Erectile Dysfunction, Too. Everyday Health. https://www.everydayhealth.com/erectile-dysfunction/young-men-get-erectile-dysfunction-too.aspx
7. NHS. 2020. Erectile dysfunction (impotence). NHS. https://www.nhs.uk/conditions/erection-problems-erectile-dysfunction/
8. Taguri, Dr. Gigi. 2019. Information on Erectile dysfunction in young men. Lloyds Pharmacy. https://onlinedoctor.lloydspharmacy.com/uk/erectile-dysfunction/erectile-dysfunction-young-men

Chapter 8: Living Life with Endometriosis

1. Grant, Rebecca. 2020. This Was Supposed to Be Endo's Big Moment. What Happened?. Cosmopolitan. https://www.cosmopolitan.com/health-fitness/a30779164/endometriosis-cure-treatment-research-government-funding/
2. NHS. 2019. Endometriosis. NHS. https://www.nhs.uk/conditions/endometriosis/complications/
3. Wynne, Lucy. 2021. Shithappenstothebestofus. https://shithappenstothebestofus.home.blog/2020/08/15/living-life-with-endometriosis/

Chapter 9: Vaginismus

1. Herdon, Jamie. 2020. What is Vaginismus? Healthline.com. https://www.healthline.com/health/vaginismus
2. Hope & Her. 2022. Vaginismus Symptoms: Variations, Examples, Problems. Hope & Her. https://hopeandher.com/pages/vaginismus-symptoms#:~:text=Depending%20on%20the%20intensity%2C%20vagini smus,closure%20of%20the%20vaginal%20opening.
3. Mayo Clinic. 2022. Painful intercourse (dyspareunia). Mayo Clinic. https://www.mayoclinic.org/diseases-conditions/painful-intercourse/symptoms-causes/syc-20375967

Chapter 10: Sexually Transmitted Infections (STIs)

1. NHS. N.d. Sexually Transmitted Infections (STIs). NHS. https://www.nhs.uk/conditions/sexually-transmitted-infections-stis/
2. Santos-Longhurst, Adrienne. 2020. The One Difference Between STIs and STDs — and How to Minimize Your Risk. Healthline. https://www.healthline.com/health/healthy-sex/sti-vs-std
3. SH:24. N.d. STI's. SH24.org. https://sh24.org.uk/sexual-health/stis

Chapter 11: Vaginas: How Much Do You Really Know?

1. Brincat, Clarissa. 2022. Why is the clit so sensitive? Thanks to over 10,000 nerves, first real count finds. Medical News Today. https://www.medicalnewstoday.com/articles/why-is-the-clit-so-sensitive-thanks-to-over-10000-nerves-first-real-count-finds
2. Moore, Lane and Ruderman, Zoe. 2020. 23 Facts You Should Know About Vaginas. Cosmopolitan. https://www.cosmopolitan.com/health-fitness/advice/a3182/vagina-facts-0110/
3. Nall, Rachel. 2020. How deep is a vagina? What to know. Medical News Today. https://www.medicalnewstoday.com/articles/321220#:~:text=The%20labi a%20majora%2C%20which%20are,if%20a%20woman%20is%20aroused.
4. RCOG. N.d. Perineal tears during childbirth. Royal College of Obstetricians and Gynaecologists. https://www.rcog.org.uk/for-the-public/perineal-tears-and-episiotomies-in-childbirth/perineal-tears-during-childbirth/#:~:text=Up%20to%209%20in%20every,are%20minor%20and%20heal%20quickly.

5. Scaccia, Annamarya. 2018. How Deep Is a Vagina? And 10 Other Things You Should Know. Healthline. https://www.healthline.com/health/womens-health/how-deep-is-a-vagina#length

6. Smith, Lorri. 2018. What's to know about interstitial cystitis? Medical News Today. https://www.medicalnewstoday.com/articles/304366

7. The Womens. N.d. Vulvodynia. The Royal Women's Hospital. https://www.thewomens.org.au/health-information/vulva-vagina/vulva-vagina-problems/vulvodynia#:~:text=Vulvodynia%20(said%20'vul%2Dvo,have%20a%20normal%2Dlooking%20vulva.

8. Wojcik, Ginger. 2020. 23 Vagina Facts You'll Want to Tell All Your Friends. Healthline. https://www.healthline.com/health/womens-health/vagina-vulva-facts

Chapter 12: Penises: How Much Do You Really Know?

1. Barhum, Lana. 2020. What is penis shrinkage and why does it happen?. Medical News Today. https://www.medicalnewstoday.com/articles/320883

2. Cartapatti, Marcelo. Destro Saade, Ricardo. Fregonesi, Adriano. Jeronimo de Oliveira Júnior, Eduardo. Marmiroli, Rafael. O. Reis, Leonardo. 2014. Mechanisms Predisposing Penile Fracture and Long-Term Outcomes on Erectile and Voiding Functions. Advances in Urology. Hindawi. https://doi.org/10.1155/2014/768158

3. Dr Felix. N.d. 20 Hard Facts About The Penis. Dr Felix. https://www.drfelix.co.uk/20-hard-facts-about-penis/

4. Gilmour, Paisley. 2021. What does cum taste like? A medical expert explains how healthy semen tastes. Cosmopolitan. https://www.cosmopolitan.com/uk/love-sex/sex/a29585978/semen-sperm-cum-taste/

5. Glamour. 2021. 39 penis facts that will blow your mind. Glamour Magazine. https://www.glamourmagazine.co.uk/gallery/penis-facts

6. Hellstrom, W.J.G. Libby, R. McCaslin, I.R Sangkum, P. Sikka, S.C. Yafi, F. 2017. 339 Grower or Shower? Predictors of Change in Penile Size From Flaccid to Erect State. Journal of Sexual Medicine. https://www.jsm.jsexmed.org/article/S1743-6095(16)30713-5/fulltext

7. Herbenick, Debby. Reece Michael. Sanders, Stephanie. Schick, Vanessa. 2013. Erect Penile Length and Circumference Dimensions of 1,661 Sexually Active Men in the United States. Journal of Sexual Medicine. https://www.jsm.jsexmed.org/article/S1743-6095(15)30537-3/fulltext

8. HER. N.d. Someone has ranked the penis size of men from all over the world. https://www.her.ie/life/someone-ranked-penis-size-men-world-306195

9. Lauriello, Samantha. 2018. 10 Weird Things You've Always Wanted to Know About Penises. Health. https://www.health.com/condition/sexual-health/penis-facts

10. Metro. 2015. Want to know which country has the biggest penises in the world? Metro. https://metro.co.uk/2015/02/28/want-to-know-which-country-has-the-biggest-penises-in-the-world-5083922/

11. Newman, Tim. 2021. 10 things you didn't know about the penis. Medical News Today. https://www.medicalnewstoday.com/articles/320748#10.

12. NHS. n.d. 5 Penis Facts. NHS. https://www.nhs.uk/live-well/sexual-health/five-penis-facts/

13. Roland, James. 2018. Can Smoking Cigarettes Cause Impotence?. Healthline. https://www.healthline.com/health/erectile-dysfunction/impotence-and-smoking

14. Shah, J and Christopher, N. 2002. Can shoe size predict penile length?. National Library of Medicine. https://pubmed.ncbi.nlm.nih.gov/12230622/

15. Sissons, Beth. 2021. Is blue balls a real condition?. Medical News Today. https://www.medicalnewstoday.com/articles/324870

16. Sparling, J. 1997. Penile erections: shape, angle, and length. National Library of Medicine. https://pubmed.ncbi.nlm.nih.gov/9292834/

17. Wynne, Lucy. 2021.The Penis - How Much Do You Know?. Sh It Happens to the Best of Us. https://shithappenstothebestofus.home.blog/2021/04/06/the-penis-how-much-do-you-know/

Chapter 13: The World of Genders and Sexualities

1. Human Rights Campaign. 2022. Marriage Equality Around the World. HRC.. https://www.hrc.org/resources/marriage-equality-around-the-world

2. Wareham, Jamie. 2020. Map Shows Where It's Illegal To Be Gay – 30 Years Since WHO Declassified Homosexuality As Disease. Forbes. https://www.forbes.com/sites/jamiewareham/2020/05/17/map-shows-where-its-illegal-to-be-gay--30-years-since-who-declassified-homosexuality-as-disease/?sh=7392b1e2578a

3. Wynne, Lucy. 2021. The World of Genders and Sexualities. Sh It Happens to the Best of Us. https://shithappenstothebestofus.home.blog/2021/06/30/the-world-of-genders-and-sexualities/

4. Zambon, Veronica. 2020. What are some different types of gender identity?. Medical News Today. https://www.medicalnewstoday.com/articles/types-of-gender-identity

Chapter 14: A Guide to Oral Sex

1. Cosmopolitan. 2021. 60 Must-Know Ways to Elevate Your Oral Sex Game. Cosmopolitan. https://www.cosmopolitan.com/sex-love/confessions/tips/a3497/oral-sex-tips/
2. Hamilton, Jill. 2020. 26 Oral Sex Positions You Need in Your Life. Cosmopolitan. https://www.cosmopolitan.com/sex-love/news/g4967/oral-sex-positions-you-need/
3. MacMillan, Amanda. 2018. 14 Things Every Woman Needs to Know About Oral Sex. Health.com. https://www.health.com/condition/sexual-health/oral-sex
4. Wynne, Lucy. 2020. Oral Sex and How Sucking D*ck Can Help Cure Depression. Sh It Happens to the Best of Us. https://shithappenstothebestofus.home.blog/2020/05/06/oral-sex-and-how-sucking-dick-can-help-cure-depression/

Chapter 15: An Introduction to Kinks and Fetishes

1. Aggrawal, Anil. 2008. Forensic and Medico-legal Aspects of Sexual Crimes and Unusual Sexual Practices. Taylor & Francis. Book.
2. American Psychiatric Association. 2013. Paraphilic Disorders. American Psychiatric Association. https://www.psychiatry.org/File%20Library/Psychiatrists/Practice/DSM/APA_DSM-5-Paraphilic-Disorders.pdf
3. Bering, Jesse. 2013. 46 Sexual Fetishes You Didn't Know Existed. Huffpost. https://www.huffpost.com/entry/sexual-fetish_n_4144418
4. Borresen, Kelsey. 2021. The Difference Between A Fetish And Kink, According To Sex Experts. Huffington Post. https://www.huffingtonpost.co.uk/entry/difference-between-fetish-and-kink_n_5b58a59ae4b0b15aba94749b
5. Emery, Lea Rose. 2016. This Is The Most Popular Fetish In The UK. Bustle. https://www.bustle.com/articles/190171-how-many-people-have-a-sexual-fetish-its-more-common-than-you-think-but-its-still

6. Kassel, Gabrielle. 2021. What's the Difference Between a Kink and a Fetish? Healthline. https://www.healthline.com/health/healthy-sex/kink-vs-fetish#difference
7. Weiss, Robert. 2017. Kinks, Fetishes, Paraphilias: Treating Issues with Non-Traditional Sexuality. Psych Central. https://psychcentral.com/blog/kinks-fetishes-paraphilias-treating-issues-with-non-traditional-sexuality#1

Chapter 16: End the Sex Toy Stigma

1. Evans, Samantha. 2015. Sex Toys for Men: Why is it Still a Taboo?. The Independent. https://www.independent.co.uk/life-style/love-sex/sex-toys-for-men-why-is-it-still-a-taboo-10304413.html
2. Ligon, Zoe. 2018. Men Shouldn't Be Ashamed of Beating Off with Sex Toys. VICE. https://www.vice.com/en/article/qvnk5q/men-shouldnt-be-ashamed-of-beating-off-with-sex-toys
3. Weiss, Suzannah. 2018. Women Are Hiding Their Sex Toys From Their Partners, But They Shouldn't Need To. Bustle. https://www.bustle.com/p/women-are-hiding-their-sex-toys-from-their-partners-but-they-shouldnt-need-to-9988077

Chapter 17: Threesomes: Are They All They Make Out to Be?

1. Frank, Katherine. 2013. Plays Well in Groups: A Journey Through the World of Group Sex. Rowman & Littlefield Publishers Inc. Page 333.
2. Hunt, Elle. 2020. The Psychology of the Threesome: Everyone Wants One, but Who's Truly Ready for it? The Guardian. https://www.theguardian.com/lifeandstyle/2020/feb/11/threesomes-men-women-sex-psychology
3. Lehmiller, Justin. 2018. Tell Me What You Want: The Science of Sexual Desire and How It Can Help You Improve Your Sex Life. Publisher: Little, Brown Book Group.
4. Levesley, David. 2019. All the Questions You Need to Ask to Have the Best Threesome Possible. GQ. https://www.gq-magazine.co.uk/article/threesome
5. N.A. 2014. 15 Things No One Tells You About Having a Threesome. Metro.https://metro.co.uk/2014/08/21/15-things-no-one-tells-you-about-having-a-threesome-4795297/?ito=cbshare

6. Schreiber, Katherine. 2016. Can You Have a Threesome and Still Have a Healthy Relationship? Greatist. https://greatist.com/live/ready-for-threesomes
7. Scoats, Ryan. 2020. Understanding Threesomes; Gender, Sex, and Consensual Non-Monogamy. Publisher: Routledge. Pages 3-11.
8. Wynne, Lucy. 2020. Threesomes: Are They All They Make Out to Be? Sh It Happens to the Best of Us. https://shithappenstothebestofus.home.blog/2020/05/23/threesomes/

Chapter 18: Fire and Ice: A Guide to Temperature Play

1. Astorino, Dominique. 2018. I Put Glass Cups of Fire on My Back to Recover From a Workout — Here's How It Went. Popsugar. https://www.popsugar.co.uk/fitness/What-Fire-Cupping-44487189
2. Brabaw, Kasandra. 2018. Fire & Ice: A How-To Guide To Temperature Sex Play. Refinery29. https://www.refinery29.com/en-us/temperature-play-sex-tips
3. Brabaw, Kasandra. 2021. The Ultimate Guide to Temperature Play. Lewandmassager. https://www.lewandmassager.com/pleasure-guide/temperature-play/
4. Gilmour, Paisley. 2017. Temperature play sex tips: A beginner's guide. Cosmopolitan. https://www.cosmopolitan.com/uk/love-sex/sex/a9904870/temperature-play-sex-ice-he
5. Glassman-Hughes, Emma. Kravitz, Jamie. 2021. 8 Tips For Using Ice During Sex That'll Make You Melt. Elite Daily. https://www.elitedaily.com/dating/ice-play-sex
6. Wynne, Lucy. 2020. Fire and Ice: A Guide To Temperature Play. Sh It Happens to the Best Of Us. https://shithappenstothebestofus.home.blog/2020/05/31/fire-and-ice-a-guide-to-temperature-play/

Chapter 19: Explained: The Spit Fetish

1. Alba, Alejandro. Grebey, James. 2014. 25 Fetishes You Probably Never Knew Existed. Buzzfeed.https://www.buzzfeed.com/alejandroalba/fetishes-you-probably-never-knew-existed

2. Griffiths, Dr Mark. 2012. The salivation army: A brief look at spit fetishes. DrMarkGriffiths. https://drmarkgriffiths.wordpress.com/2012/06/28/the-salivation-army-a-brief-look-at-spit-fetishes/
3. Lehmiller, Justin. 2018. Tell Me What You Want: The Science of Sexual Desire and How it Can Help You Improve Your Sex Life. Robinson.
4. Santos, Romano. 2022. How To Make a Person With a Spit Kink Really Happy. Vice. https://www.vice.com/en/article/4awmdj/how-to-make-person-spit-kink-happy-bdsm-fetish-sex-consent
5. Wynne, Lucy . 2020. EXPLAINED: The Spit Fetish. Sh It Happens to the Best Of Us. https://shithappenstothebestofus.home.blog/2020/07/01/explained-the-spit-fetish/

Chapter 20: The Foot Fetish

1. Bell, James. 2020. There is scientific proof that foot fetishes are normal. Bigthink.com. https://bigthink.com/health/psychology-of-foot-fetishes/#rebelltitem4
2. Enquist, M. Ghirlanda,S. Jannini, EA. Scorolli,C. Zattoni, S. 2007. Relative prevalence of different fetishes. Nature. https://www.nature.com/articles/3901547
3. Holland, Kimberly. 2019. Everything You Need to Know About Foot Fetishes. Healthline. https://www.healthline.com/health/foot-fetish
4. Lehmiller, Justin and Zane, Zachary. 2020. How Common Are Foot Fetishes, and Why Do People Have Them? Men's Health. https://www.menshealth.com/sex-women/a19523651/foot-fetish/
5. McManus, M. A., Hargreaves, P., Rainbow, L., & Alison, L. J. 2013. Paraphilias: definition, diagnosis and treatment. Faculty Opinions. https://doi.org/10.12703/p5-36
6. Psychology Today. N.d. Paraphilias. Psychology Today. https://www.psychologytoday.com/gb/conditions/paraphilias
7. Wolchover, Natalie. 2011. Why Do People Have Foot Fetishes? Live Science. https://www.livescience.com/33525-foot-fetishes-toe-suck-fairy.html
8. Wynne, Lucy. 2020. The Foot Fetish. Sh It Happens to the Best of Us. https://shithappenstothebestofus.home.blog/2020/04/08/the-foot-fetish/

Chapter 21: BDSM and Safe Practice

1. Holland, Kimberly. 2019. Everything You Need to Know About Erotic Asphyxiation. Healthline. https://www.healthline.com/health/healthy-sex/erotic-asphyxiation#safety

2. Jalili, Candice. 2019. 12 Safe Word Options and How to Effectively Use One in the Bedroom. Cosmopolitan. https://www.cosmopolitan.com/sex-love/a29869328/safe-words-for-sex-bdsm/

3. Shea, Alex. 2021. Let's Talk About Choking During Sex. Shape. https://www.shape.com/lifestyle/sex-and-love/lets-talk-about-choking-during-sex

4. Smith, Gabrielle. 2020. Everything to Know About BDSM Aftercare—and 10 Ways to Do It After Sex. Men's Health. https://www.menshealth.com/sex-women/a29341534/sexual-aftercare/

5. Wynne, Lucy. 2020. 'Ropeplay and Bondage. Sh It Happens to the Best of Us. https://shithappenstothebestofus.home.blog/2020/04/03/ropeplay-and-bondage/

6. Wynne, Lucy. 2020. BDSM and Safe Practice. Sh It Happens to the Best of Us. https://shithappenstothebestofus.home.blog/2020/01/12/bdsm-and-safe-practice/

Chapter 22: Water Sports: Everything You Need to Know

1. Molloy, Antonia. 2014. How Common Is Your Sexual Fantasy? The Independent. https://www.independent.co.uk/life-style/health-and-families/health-news/how-common-is-your-sexual-fantasy-9835480.html

2. N.A. 2016. These are the 10 Most Popular Sexual Fetishes in the UK. Indy 100: The Independent. https://www.indy100.com/viral/the-10-most-popular-sexual-fetishes-in-the-uk-7291981

3. N.A. 2017. Why Some People Enjoy 'Watersports' - And What It's Really Like. Esquire. https://www.esquire.com/uk/life/sex-relationships/news/a12429/why-some-people-like-watersports-and-what-its-really-like/

4. Shere. Jeremy. 2011. Is It Ok to Drink Urine? Indiana Public Media. https://indianapublicmedia.org/amomentofscience/drink-urine.php

5. Smothers. Hannah. 2016. Golden Shower. Cosmopolitan. .https://www.cosmopolitan.com/sexopedia/a13091141/golden-shower-facts/#:~:text=A%20golden%20shower%2C%20also%20called,near%2Fin%2Ffront%20of%20you.

6. Thorpe, JR. 2017. The Psychology Of Peeing Fetishes. Bustle. https://www.bustle.com/p/the-psychology-of-peeing-fetishes-if-those-donald-allegations-had-you-wondering-29603

7. UberKinky. N.d. Read Our Beginner's Guide to Watersports. Uber Kinky. https://www.uberkinky.co.uk/essential-guides/beginners-guide-to-water-sports.html
8. Wynne, Lucy. 2020. Watersports: Everything You Need to Know. Sh It Happens to the Best of Us. https://shithappenstothebestofus.home.blog/2020/07/12/water-sports-everything-you-need-to-know/

Chapter 23: Sex and… Periods

1. Chalabi, Mona. 2017. Going with the flow: how your period affects your sex drive. The Guardian. https://www.theguardian.com/lifeandstyle/2016/oct/15/how-period-affects-sex-drive-menstruation-ovulation
2. NHS. N.d. Hepatitis. NHS. https://www.nhs.uk/conditions/Hepatitis/
3. NHS. N.d. Periods. NHS. https://www.nhs.uk/conditions/periods/
4. O'Keefe Osborn, Corinne. 2019. Am I Allergic to Condoms? Symptoms and Treatment. Healthline. https://www.healthline.com/health/healthy-sex/allergic-to-condom
5. Watson, Stephanie. 2021. Is It Safe to Have Sex During Your Period? Tips, Benefits, and Side Effects. Healthline. https://www.healthline.com/health/womens-health/sex-during-periods#pregnancy
6. Wynne, Lucy. 2020. Sex and…. Periods. Sh It Happens to the Best of Us. https://shithappenstothebestofus.home.blog/2020/04/25/sex-and-periods/

Chapter 24: Anal Sex… Shit Happens

1. Breslaw, Anna. Hsieh, Carina. Varina, Rachel. 2022. A Complete Beginner's Guide to Anal Sex. Cosmopolitan. https://www.cosmopolitan.com/sex-love/advice/a6676/anal-sex-beginners-guide/
2. Hsieh, Carina and Sullivan, Corinne. 2022. 17 Best Lubes for Anal Play (Because We Know You're Curious). Cosmopolitan. https://www.cosmopolitan.com/sex-love/a13517603/best-anal-lube/

3. Migala, Jessica. 2020. How Likely Are You To Poop During Anal Sex?. Women's Health. https://www.womenshealthmag.com/sex-and-love/a19983292/poop-during-anal-sex/
4. Santos-Longhurst, Adrienne. 2022. Anal Sex Safety: Everything You Need to Know. Healthline. https://www.healthline.com/health/healthy-sex/anal-sex-safety#what-it-is
5. Santos-Longhurst, Adrienne. 2019. A Beginner's Guide to Anal Douching. Healthline. https://www.healthline.com/health/anal-douche#benefits

Milton Keynes UK
Ingram Content Group UK Ltd.
UKHW020611010823
426133UK00011B/338